WHERE'S THE UNICORN POO?

ORCHARD

ORCHARD BOOKS

First published in Great Britain in 2019

by The Watts Publishing Group

9 10 8

© 2021 The Watts Publishing Group Limited

Illustrations by Dynamo Limited

Additional images © Shutterstock

A CIP catalogue record for this book is available from the British Library

ISBN 978 1 40836 120 7

Printed and bound in China

FSC
www.fsc.org

MIX
Paper from
responsible sources
FSC® C104740

Orchard Books
An imprint of Hachette Children's Group
Part of The Watts Publishing Group Limited
Carmelite House
50 Victoria Embankment
London EC4Y 0DZ

An Hachette UK Company
www.hachette.co.uk
www.hachettechildrens.co.uk

WHERE'S THE UNICORN POO?

THE MOST MAGICAL POOS YOU'VE EVER SEEN

The unicorn poos are going on an adventure to a fairytale castle, a petting zoo and even into space!

Can you spot each of the poos in every scene?

See if you can spot Snowdrop in one of the scenes, too!

GARY

the Green Goo Poo is the squishiest and slimiest of all the poos.

MOLLY

the Magic Poo shines brightly wherever she goes and spreads magic with her unicorn poo friends. She is truly special.

LUNA

No star could sparkle as much as Luna, the Midnight Poo. She really is the most glamorous poo there ever was.

POPPY

the Princess Poo is the fanciest of the poos. She expects lots of bowing and curtseying wherever she goes. She is unicorn poo royalty!

RAYMOND

the Rainbow Poo is super-groovy. He's the joker of the group and is always ready to party and have a good time.

PETTING ZOO

The poos are having a day out at the petting zoo. Luna's favourite animal is a llama – what's yours?

CARNIVAL CHAOS

The unicorn poos are joining in the parade. Spot them amongst the dancing and partying.

SNOWDROP STAMPEDE

The unicorn poos are hiding behind the many Snowdrops. Can you find them all?

Odd one out!

Can you spot the unicorn that looks different to the rest?

ONCE UPON A TIME...

Poppy feels at home in the fairytale land. Can you spot where Poppy and her friends have got to?

OUT OF THIS WORLD

The unicorn poos are exploring outer space among the rockets, aliens and astronauts.

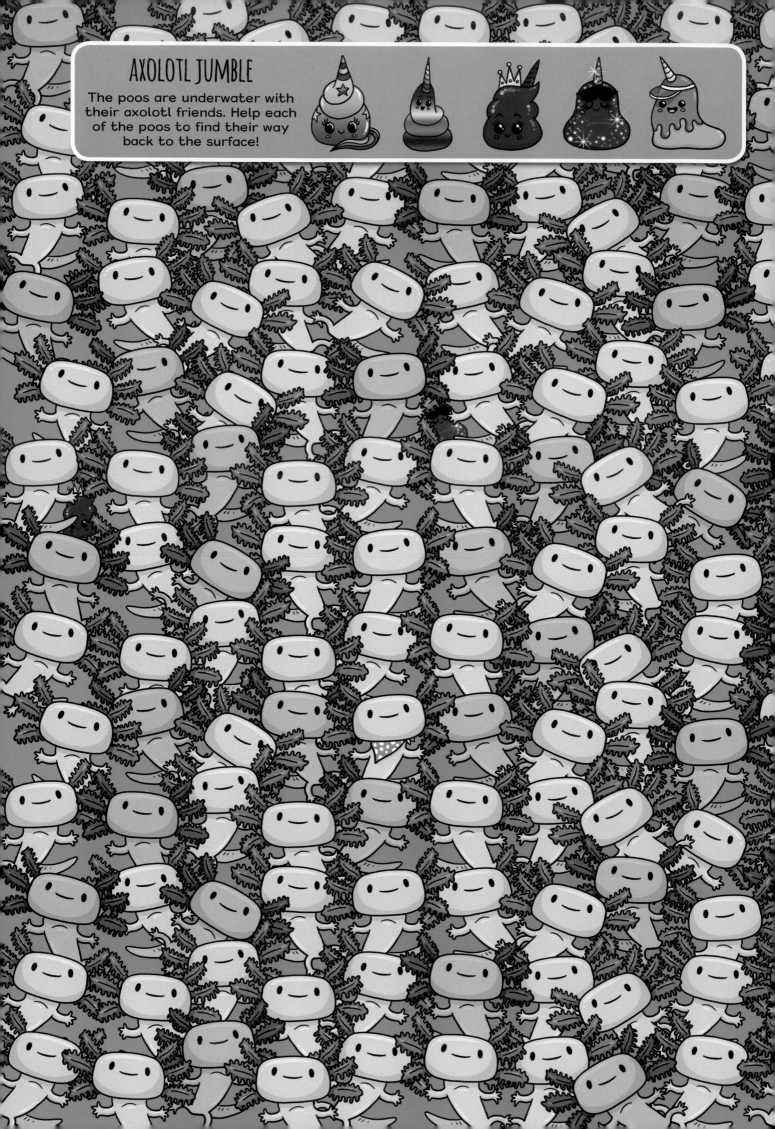

AXOLOTL JUMBLE

The poos are underwater with their axolotl friends. Help each of the poos to find their way back to the surface!

Odd one out!

Can you spot the axolotl that looks different to the rest?

DINOSAUR LAND

Molly feels very small next to her new dinosaur friends. Find the poos before the Tyrannosaurus rex gets hungry!

MUSIC FESTIVAL

It's a beautiful day and the poos are all enjoying the festival. Luna is getting her face painted! Spot her and her friends.

LLAMA LAND

The unicorn poos are surrounded by llamas. Can you spot all the poos?

Odd one out!

Can you spot the llama that looks different to the rest?

POO PIER

The unicorn poos are having a day out by the sea. Can you spot what each of them is getting up to?

TOY SHOP

Everyone inside the shop is searching for their favourite toy. But can you find your favourite unicorn poo?

DIZZY DINOSAURS

What a lot of dinosaurs! Can you find each of the unicorn poos in amongst them?

FROZEN FRIENDS

The poos are visiting their friends from the Arctic and Antarctic. Find them all before they freeze.

SPRING BLOSSOM

Molly is relaxing in the garden whilst Raymond admires the water. Can you spot each of the poos in the scene?

ANSWERS

Now try and find these extra items in each scene!

PETTING ZOO

A ginger cat ☐

Thirteen carrots ☐

Four cabbages ☐

A pink llama ☐

A goose chasing a girl ☐

A boy wearing a dinosaur T-shirt ☐

Two weather vanes ☐

A man pushing a pram ☐

A sleepy hedgehog ☐

Five squirrels ☐

CARNIVAL CHAOS

A tambourine ☐

Four umbrellas ☐

An orange heart balloon ☐

Four unicorn headbands ☐

A man riding a unicycle ☐

A juggling clown ☐

Three wheelchairs ☐

A loudhailer ☐

A trumpet ☐

A giant honeypot ☐

SNOWDROP STAMPEDE

ONCE UPON A TIME . . .

A wolf wearing a red cape ☐

Humpty Dumpty ☐

Five pumpkins ☐

Two swords stuck in stones ☐

Seven mice wearing neckerchiefs ☐

Two green owls ☐

A magic genie lamp ☐

A spider ☐

Two mermaids ☐

Three treasure chests ☐

OUT OF THIS WORLD

- An apple tree ☐
- Three flags ☐
- A purple alien with three eyes ☐
- Two cats in space suits ☐
- An orange monster with purple spots ☐
- Five baseball hats ☐
- Two telescopes ☐
- An astronaut with pink hair ☐
- Five rainbow shooting stars ☐
- A red alien with five eyes ☐

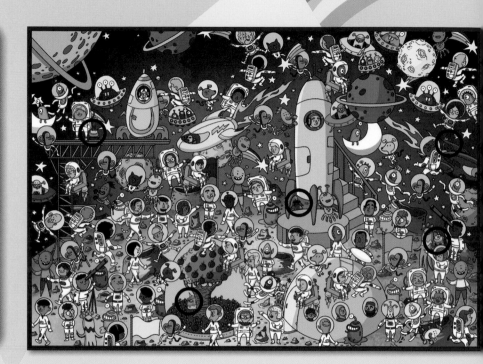

AXOLOTL JUMBLE

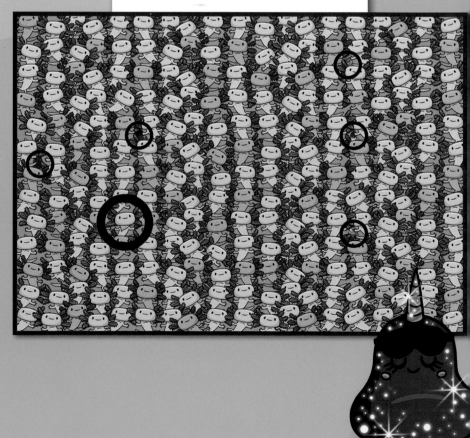

DINOSAUR LAND

Six dinosaur eggs ☐

Two campfires ☐

Four palm trees ☐

Eleven bone hair accessories ☐

Four pterodactyls ☐

Two erupting volcanoes ☐

Five skulls ☐

Seven tiny green lizards ☐

Two purple triceratops ☐

A cavewoman wearing pink with a club ☐

MUSIC FESTIVAL

A boy with blue hair ☐

Two picnic baskets ☐

A face-painting clown ☐

A hula hoop ☐

A diabolo ☐

An ice cream balloon ☐

A purple deck chair ☐

A dog ☐

A boy with a sunshine T-shirt ☐

A girl playing the clarinet ☐

LLAMA LAND

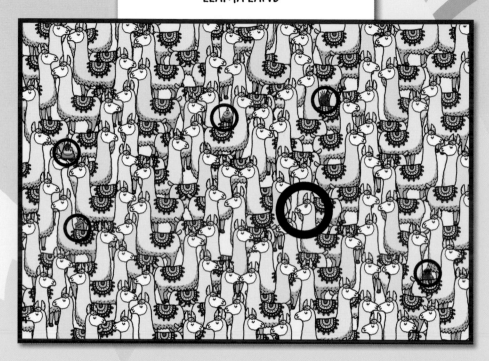

POO PIER

A cat wearing a pirate's hat ☐

A dog bowl ☐

Two pairs of binoculars ☐

A mermaid figurehead ☐

Four sea lions ☐

A starfish ☐

A fish sitting on a bench ☐

A box of worms ☐

A coil of rope ☐

Six safety rings ☐